About this book

Your child can learn to recognize and draw shapes using this book.

Always give your child plenty of praise and encouragement. The more your child enjoys the activities, the more likely they are to learn and develop a love of learning.

Your child does not need to complete each page in one go – they can come back to it another time. Always stop before your child gets tired.

The first few pages of the book are for your child to practise drawing different kinds of lines to help with pen control.

How to hold your pen

These pictures show how to hold a pen correctly. Young children often take a long time to master pen control.

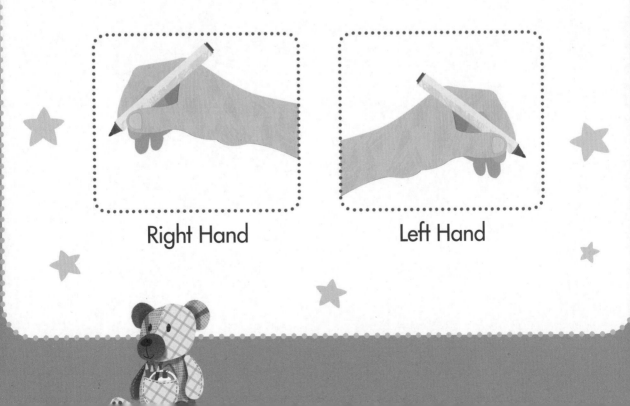

Right Hand   Left Hand

Fun with Shapes

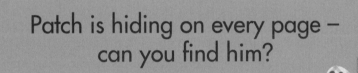

Patch is hiding on every page – can you find him?

A LAUGHING LOBSTER BOOK 978-1-910765-72-2

Published in Great Britain by Laughing Lobster
an imprint of Centum Publishing Ltd.
This edition published 2021.
1 3 5 7 9 10 8 6 4 2

Illustrations by Julia Seal.

Laughing Lobster an imprint of Centum Publishing Ltd, 20 Devon Square,
Newton Abbot, Devon, TQ12 2HR, UK
books@centumpublishingltd.co.uk
LAUGHING LOBSTER AN IMPRINT OF CENTUM PUBLISHING
Limited Reg. No. 08497203

A CIP catalogue record for this book is available from the British Library.

Printed in China.

Answers are at the back of the book!

Drawing Straight Lines

Before we begin to draw shapes, let's practise using our pen. Trace the straight lines.

Hold your pen like this:

right-handed

left-handed

Jessie

strawberry

Amelia

banana

Charlie

apple

Drawing Diagonal Lines

Now it's time to draw diagonal lines. Help Alfie, Amelia, Charlie and Jessie draw the rows of lines from bottom to top and top to bottom.

Double check your pen position using the pictures on the previous page.

Alfie

Charlie

Amelia

Jessie

Draw your own diagonal lines.

Drawing Wavy Lines

Woah! Look at these wavy lines the bouncy ball has made.
Can you help Amelia and Alfie trace them all using your pen?

Alfie

Amelia

Now try tracing this looping line the butterfly has made.

Drawing Zigzag Lines

Jessie is racing her favourite toys. Trace the zigzag lines from the things that go to the finish flags.

Which one do you think was the slowest?

train

car

truck

tractor

Friendly Faces

Draw around these friendly animal faces.

Give each animal a sweet name!

cat

bear

dog

guinea pig

Round and Round

Help Charlie get to the ice cream at the centre of this spiral by tracing the line from start to finish.

START

Square Spiral

Uh-oh! Help Amelia catch the runaway cat by tracing the line from start to finish.

START

What a Mess!

Alfie has got his yo-yo string in such a muddle. Trace the muddled line to help him unravel it.

START

All About Squares

Squares have four equal sides. Let's draw a square.

Look

Trace

Draw it on your own.

Practise your squares here:

Spot the Square!

Help Amelia find the one square in this group of shapes.

All About Triangles

Triangles have three sides. Let's draw a triangle.

Look   Trace   Draw it on your own.

Practise your triangles here:

Odd One Out

Help Alfie find the one shape that is not a triangle.

All About Rectangles

Rectangles have two long sides and two shorter sides. Let's draw a rectangle.

Look   Trace   Draw it on your own.

Practise your rectangles here:

Rectangle or Square?

Help Charlie find three rectangles amongst all the squares. Mark each rectangle with your pen.

All About Circles

Circles don't have any sides as they are completely round. Let's draw a circle.

Look

Trace

Draw it on your own.

Practise your circles here:

Flowers in a Row

Help Jessie draw some flowers by tracing the circles.

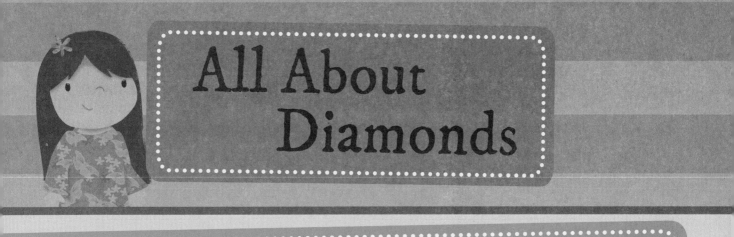

All About Diamonds

Diamonds are like squares as they also have four equal sides. Let's draw a diamond.

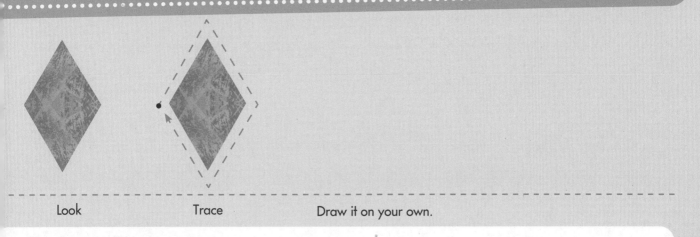

Look

Trace

Draw it on your own.

Practise your diamonds here:

Fly a kite!

Alfie and Amelia are flying diamond-shaped kites. Draw one for Amelia.

All About Stars

Stars have five points. Let's draw a star.

Look   Trace   Draw it on your own.

Practise your stars here:

Sweet Stars

Jessie is adding sweet faces to these stars she has drawn. Add your own sweet doodles.

All About Ovals

Ovals are like stretched circles. Let's draw an oval.

Look   Trace   Draw it on your own.

Practise your ovals here:

Oval or Circle?

Help Charlie find three ovals amongst all the circles. Mark each oval with your pen.

All About Pentagons

Pentagons have five equal sides. Let's draw a pentagon.

Look   Trace   Draw it on your own.

Practise your pentagons here:

Pentagon Patterns

Help Alfie add some doodle patterns to these pentagon shapes.

All About Hexagons

Hexagons have six equal sides. Let's draw a hexagon.

Look   Trace   Draw it on your own.

Practise your hexagons here:

Spot the Hexagon!

Help Amelia find the one hexagon in this group of shapes.

All About Crescents

Crescents have two points and two curves. Let's draw a crescent.

Look   Trace   Draw it on your own.

Practise your crescents here:

The Moon is Out!

Help Charlie draw a crescent moon shape in this starry sky.

All About Hearts

Hearts are sweet shapes than mean love and friendship. Let's draw a heart.

Look   Trace   Draw it on your own.

Practise your hearts here:

Hearts for Everyone

Draw a heart for each of the friends in the boxes.

Amelia

Alfie

Jessie

Charlie

All About Crosses

Crosses look like two lines crossing one another. Let's draw a cross.

Look   Trace   Draw it on your own.

Practise your crosses here:

Cross or Star?

Help Jessie find three crosses amongst the stars. Mark each cross with your pen.

All About Arrows

Arrows can show you the way to go. Let's draw an arrow.

Look   Trace   Draw it on your own.

Practise your arrows here:

Which Way?

a. ←
b. →
c. ↑
d. ↓

We use arrows on signs. Which sign shows an **up** arrow?

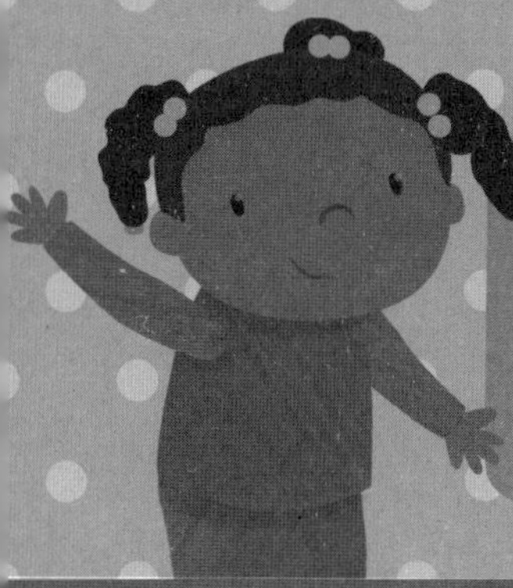

Shape Counting

Count each group, then write the number total in the box.

Which group has the **most**?

Which group has the **least**?

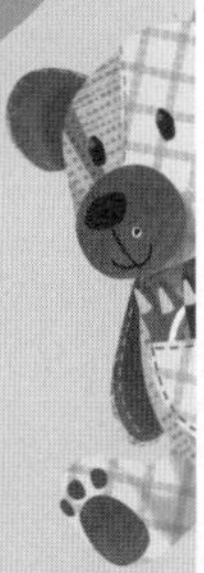

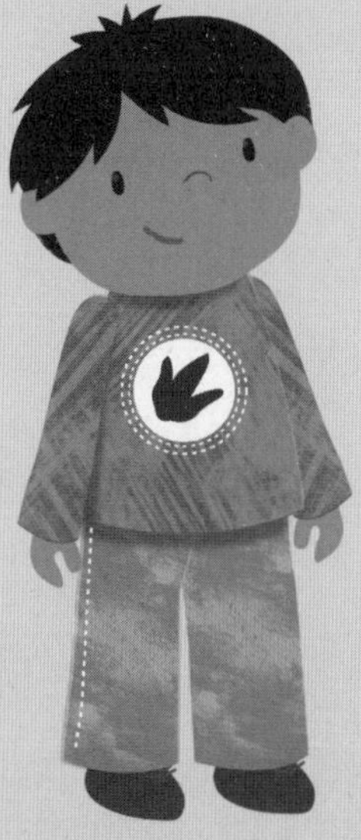

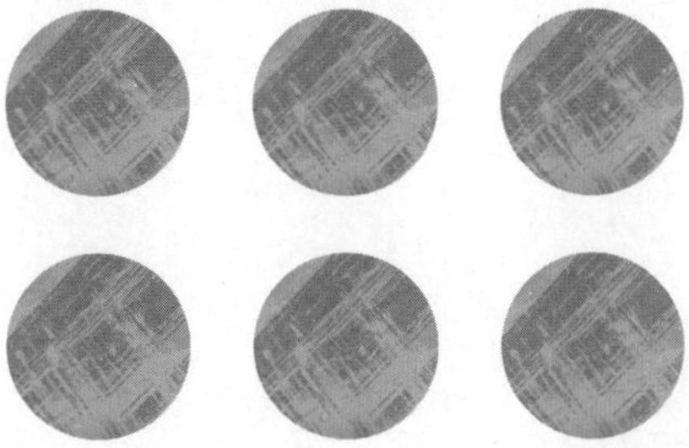

circles

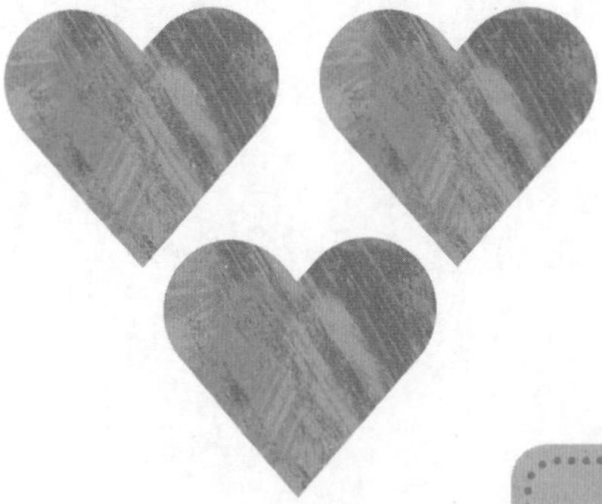

hearts

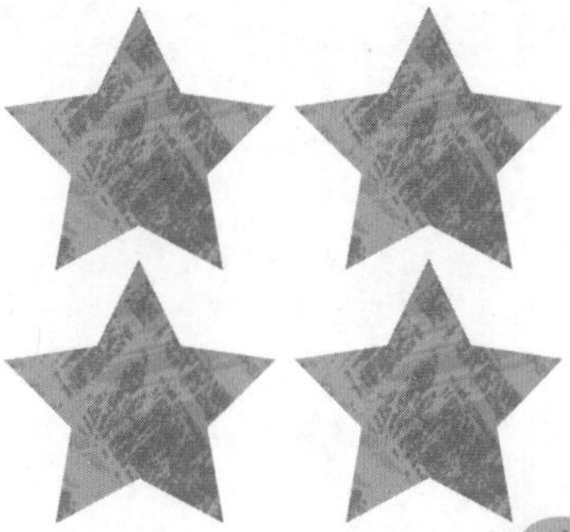

stars

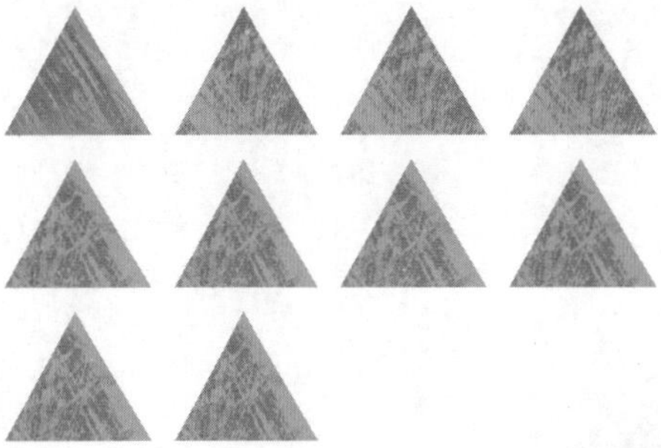

triangles

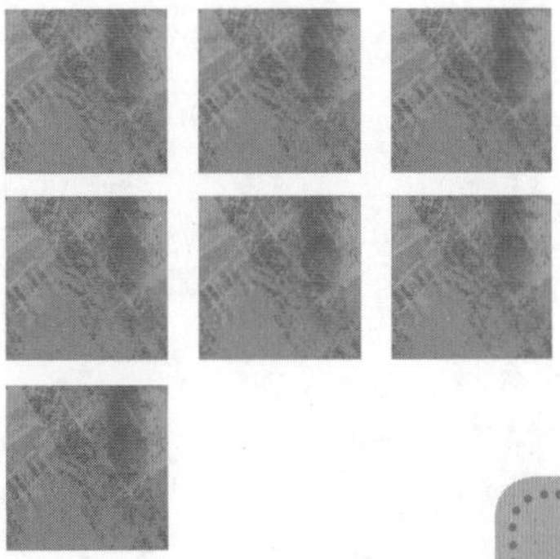

squares

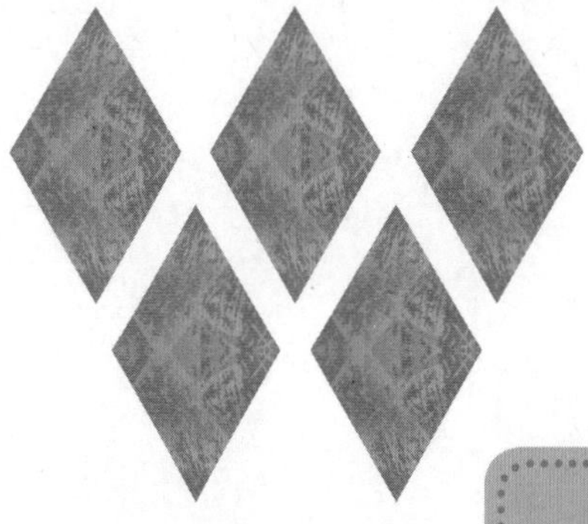

diamonds

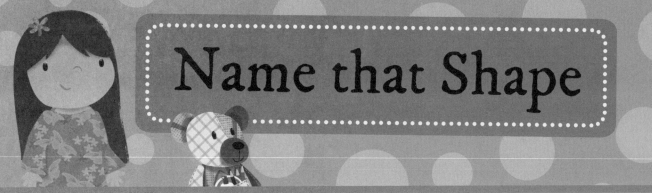

Name that Shape

Now you know how to draw shapes, let's learn to write their names. Trace the letters.

First, write the word "Shape".

shape

diamond

oval

square

star

triangle

circle

rectangle

Name that Shape

pentagon   heart

hexagon   arrow

crescent   cross

Draw a picture of your
favourite shape here.

Hide and Seek Shapes

Can you help the friends find all the shapes hiding in this picture? There are six to find. When you find a shape mark it with your pen and tick it off in the box below.

Big and Little

Can you help Charlie find the biggest shape on this page and then help Jessie find the smallest?

Shape Maze

Can you help Alfie find his way through the maze from start to finish and collect five arrows on the way?

START

FINISH

Shape Artist

It's time for art class at school and Jessie is decorating shapes. Can you help her using your doodles?

Shape Quiz

Check your answers on page 32. What did you score out of 10?

Now you know your shapes so well, answer this shapes quiz!

1. What shape is this pizza?

    _____

2. What shapes are on this butterfly's wings?

    _____

3. Which shape is like a kite?

    _____

4. What shape means love?

    _____

5. Which shape can show you the way?

    _____

6. Which of these is an oval?

    a.   b.

    _____

7. What shapes can you see on this ball?

    _____

8. What shape is this banana similar to?

    _____

9. What shapes can you see on this flag?

    _____

10. What shape are the car's wheels?

    _____

Answers

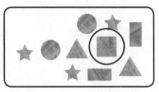

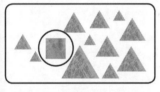

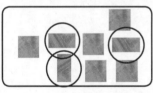

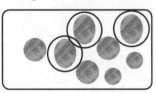

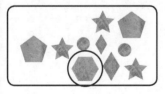

c

Circles 6, Stars 4, Hearts 3, Triangles 10, Squares 7, Diamonds 5
Most: Triangles   Least: Hearts

1. Circle
2. Stars
3. Diamond
4. Heart
5. Arrow
6. b
7. Pentagons
8. Crescent
9. Squares
10. Circles